D1597250

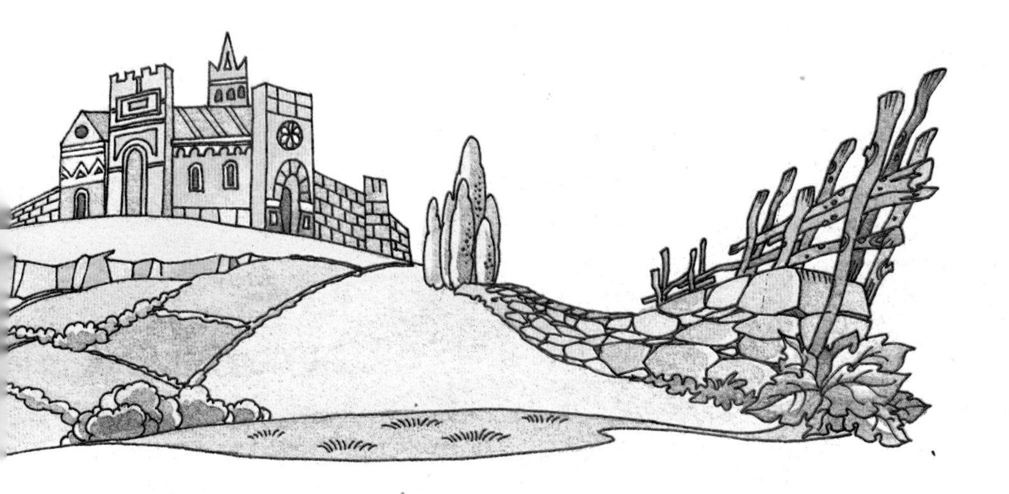

ALBA · HOUSE NEW · YORK
SOCIETY OF ST. PAUL, 2187 VICTORY BLVD., STATEN ISLAND, NEW YORK 10314

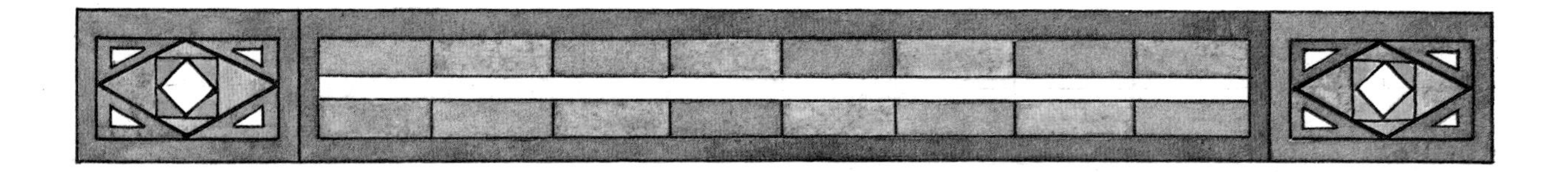

the true story of the Manger

Concept and Text by Antonio Tarzia
Illustrations by Gino Gavioli
Translated by Edmund C. Lane, S.S.P.

alba house

ISBN 0-8189-0541-7
Printed: 1988
Amilcare Pizzi Sp.A.,
Cinisello Balsamo (Milan)

Papa, this year our manger is going to be more beautiful than ever! The stable is as big as a church and the first little lamb to arrive is just waiting for the piper to play.

— How I wish that along with the ox and the ass there might also be some lions and tigers and eagles.

— We don't have any, but there would still be room for them. And you can be sure that they would get along. In the manger there is no such thing as violence, so you can

put a robin redbreast next to the cat, the lamb next to the wolf. The world of the manger is a world of peace.

— Papa, the angel of glory is missing, too. Last year it got broken. Without the angel, who will announce to the shepherds that Jesus is born?

— Grandpa is going to bring the angel along with the starry sky that we'll put behind the shed. He's also going to bring the comet which went before the Magi kings on their journey from the East.

— I wish that we could make a tiny little lake and fill it with the goldfish that I have up in my room.

— Goldfish don't fit in too well in the manger scene because they need a lot of care. And then, too, since they are alive, they move, whereas the manger scene is something frozen in time, like a photograph. It's meant to call to mind that instant in which, according to tradition, time stood still out of wonder, and there was a great silence throughout the earth because in Bethlehem Jesus, God as a baby,[1] was born.

— Is this in the Gospels, Papa?

— No, my child. An ancient tradition tells us this. The Gospel of Luke says only that Mary — the mother of Jesus — and Joseph her husband were in Bethlehem "when the time came for her to have her child, and she gave birth to her firstborn son. She wrapped him in swaddling clothes and laid him in a manger, because there was no room for them in the inn. Now there were shepherds in that region living in the fields and keeping the night watch over their flock."[2] An angel bathed in light appeared to them and announced that an extraordinary child had been born who was called the Messiah and Lord. Other angels filled the heavens, praising God and singing: "Glory to God in the highest and on earth peace to those on whom his favor rests."[3]

— Are the ox and the ass in the Gospels?

— They are named in Scripture but not in the story of the events that took place in Bethlehem. An ancient prophecy of Isaiah spoke of these two peaceful, hardworking domestic animals.[4] By tradition, the early Christians placed them near the grotto together with the shepherds

and their sheep.
— Papa! Grandpa's here! And he's brought the angel of glory with him. Mamma's saying that lunch is ready. Grandpa, after lunch will you tell us the story of the manger and speak to us about the Magi kings?
— Okay, okay. But only a little later.

Many long years ago, in order to experience more vividly the feast of the Nativity and to live it with greater devotion, Christians began to stage those pages of the Gospel where the facts regarding the birth of Jesus are recounted.

They went from a simple reading of the Gospel to a holy representation of it with real people and at times real animals. The costumes which they wore were similar to those illustrated in the mosaics they saw in church and in the bas-reliefs of many tombs. The sacred text was recited and sung as it might be in a theater, though in a different spirit. The result was often so exceptional that many coming from other lands or even from the environs around the city itself wanted to see it. There were many repeat performances and people spoke at length about them.

Some even thought to perpetuate the Nativity throughout the year by sculpting the figures of Bethlehem in wood or marble. In the basilica of Saint Mary Major in Rome, for example, one can admire to this day a priceless replica of a manger scene done in marble during the 1200s. The life-size statues were done by Arnolfo di Cambio. Among them we find the kneeling Madonna with her child, St. Joseph, the ox and the ass. In front of the Madonna there is one of the Magi prostrate in adoration while the other two, who are standing, offer their gifts. But the manger scene as we have come to know it, with the grotto at the center and all the figures facing the baby Jesus, was the invention of the nature-loving, optimistic saint, Francis of Assisi, who preached to the swallows and warmly greeted the sheep and their lambs. In the manger scene, Francis created a small and ideal world, which can be built with one's own hands but which must be recreated each year following the little laws that govern all such symbols. Otherwise the manger will not bear a message but will become just another pastime.

We read in the chronicles of those days that — some time before he intoned his *Canticle of the Creatures* in which, giving voice to the elements, he

praised God for brother sun and sister moon, for brother wind and sister water, for brother fire and sister death — Francis put together at Greccio, near the town of Rieti, the very first manger.[5]

Francis was famous throughout the Christian world for the life which he was leading. From the time when he despoiled himself of his clothes before the bishop to give them back to

his father, many young people left their belongings and professions to follow him in his ideal of poverty. He spoke of the Gospel with such enthusiasm that the people and even the birds used to listen to him attentively.

In the year 1210 he went to see Pope Honorius III in Rome. There he asked the Holy Father to approve his Rule of life with his

brothers, in absolute poverty, preaching the Gospel in simplicity. The Pope praised his new way of being a Christian and gave him permission to found a religious family.

While everyone else was thinking of war and how to get even for real or presumed wrongs, he left for the Orient in 1219, a crusader armed only with the pardon and the word of Jesus. He was received by

the Sultan al-Malik al-Kamil and was able to visit in peace the holy places associated with the life of the Lord. His strongest recollections of this trip revolved around the grotto in Bethlehem where the Lord willed to be born in poverty.

One day a nobleman by the name of John ran into Francis and asked him what he ought to do to follow the ways of the Lord. Francis told him to get himself ready and to prepare for the Nativity. And so this man had a stable built, straw procured and an ass and an ox brought in. Then December came. . . .

On Christmas night in 1223 many shepherds and farmers, artisans and poor people wended their way towards the grotto[6] which John of Greccio had prepared for Francis. Some brought gifts to offer in homage to the Baby and to share with the poorest of the poor.

Anno Domini 1223

Francis said that he wanted to celebrate a new rite, one that would be more meaningful and in which there would be greater participation on the part of the people. For this, he asked permission of the Pope. He invited a priest who celebrated Mass on an improvised altar. And Francis, surrounded by his friars, sang the Gospel.

He remained before the crib, filled with piety and overflowing with joy while tears ran down his cheeks.[7] After the singing of the Gospel, Francis spoke. "Brothers," he said, "this is the Feast of feasts.

Today God makes himself a tiny infant and nurses at the breast of a woman." The emotion of the moment was such that Francis felt like a baby himself and began to babble, as if he were in fact a child.[8]

At that point there was seen, "sleeping inside the manger, a beautiful little infant which the blessed Francis, holding close to himself with both his arms, seemed to wake from sleep."[9] Among the witnesses of this miracle were many persons worthy of trust and these aided in spreading the news in all of central Italy — as far north as Genoa and as far south as Naples — wherever there where monasteries and convents celebrating the Nativity.

Many drew spiritual and physical benefits from that miracle. Some were converted and became better people. Others took the straw from the manger of Greccio and used it as a medicine against the maladies of man and beast. One woman, in travail during a difficult labor, found strength and peace.

Happily, a child was born and a feast was thrown for all in the house. The whole countryside came to know of this event and treasured the memory of that night when a Baby appeared to Francis who wanted to reconstruct in the Apennine woods the atmosphere of that first Christmas.

Life was serenely taken up again in the convents where the friends of Francis dwelt, in the homes of the farmers and in the city where Francis went to preach peace to opposing factions and hostile

families. One day in December a friar asked Francis "if it was obligatory to abstain from meat on Christmas, since that year it fell on Friday."[10]

With gentle firmness, Francis declared, "It is wrong, my brother, to consider the day on which the Child Jesus was born for us a Friday."[11] It is rather a great feast, he said. And he recommended that on that day an abundance of food might even be given to our animal friends and that the ox and the ass might receive a double ration of corn and oats.[12]

His teaching was embraced by farm dweller and city folk alike. Often the young girls of the vicinity where Francis had passed could be seen scattering grain and wheat to the wind and on the road so that the larks and robins, the wrens and wild doves would never have to suffer from want of food.

السلام
天主在享光荣
良人在享平安
GLORIA A DIO
E PACE AGLI UOMINI
Glory to God
and peace to m
СЛАВА БОГУ И
МИР ЛЮДЯМ

المجدُ للهِ في
والرجاء

This is the true story of the manger. Now let us put up the heavens with the star, the snow on the mountains and the trees, along with the angel of glory.

— Grandpa, why does the angel carry a banner with strange writing on it this year?

— It's the usual saying: "Glory to God in the highest and on earth peace to those upon whom his favor rests." Only this time it's in English, Russian, Arabic and Chinese.

— But do you know Chinese, Grandpa?

— No, and not even Russian or Arabic. But Jesus is the friend of children the world over and speaks of peace in every language and place.

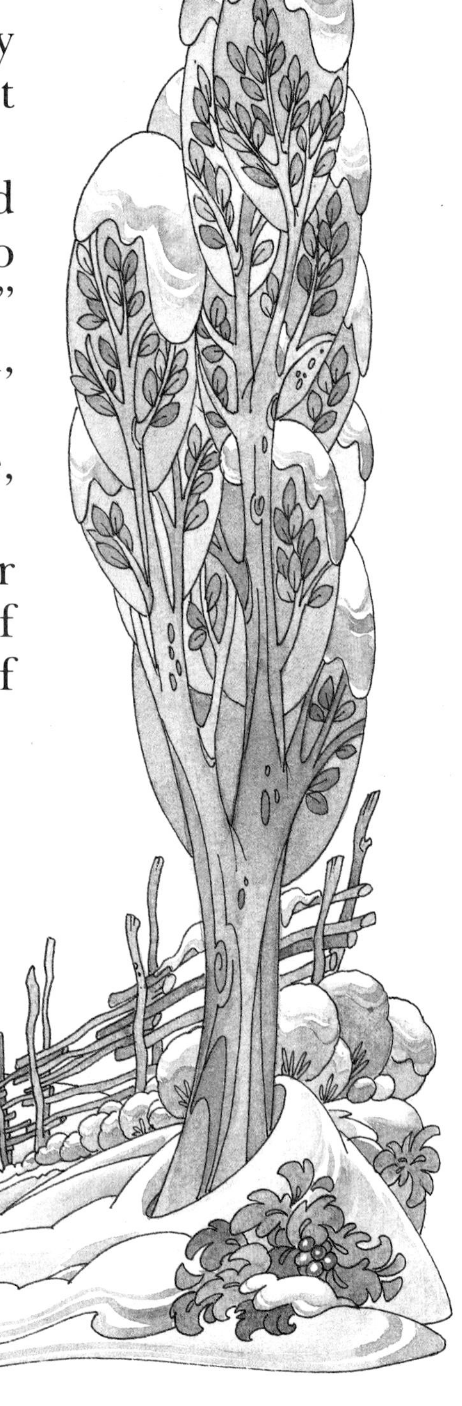

GINO GAVIOLI

Gino Gavioli, a serious and versatile professional artist, was born in Milan in 1923. After having frequented the Academy of Brera, he entered the world of cartoons. The war interrupted his activity for several years. In 1952, together with his brother Robert and Paul Piffarerio, he founded a society for the production of animated cartoons, *Gamma Film*, which produces some full-length and many spot ads with unforgettable main characters. He has collaborated in the publication of *Giornalino*, an Italian childrens' magazine, since 1959 and has provided the illustrations for several Italian Pauline publications including *The Tales of Hans Christian Andersen, A Thousand and One Nights, Robin Hood*, and *Alice in Wonderland* among many others.

Notes

1. The Protogospel of James 12:2.
2. Luke 2:6-8.
3. Luke 2:14.
4. Isaiah 1:3.
5. Bonaventure of Bagnoregio, *Legenda major X*, 7.1.
6. Bonaventure of Bagnoregio, *Legenda major X*, 7.2.
7. Bonaventure of Bagnoregio, *Legenda major X*, 7.4.
8. Thomas of Celano, *Vita II*, 199.1.
9. Bonaventure of Bagnoregio, *Legenda major X*, 7.6.
10. Thomas of Celano, *Vita II*, 199.2.
11. *Ibid.*
12. Thomas of Celano, *Vita II*, 200.1